GRAFFITI DOODLE

Mess Up a Masterpiece

GRAFFITI DOODLE

Mess Up a Masterpiece

ANDREW PINDER

MICHAEL O'MARA BOOKS LIMITED

First published in Great Britain in 2011 by
Michael O'Mara Books Limited
9 Lion Yard
Tremadoc Road
London SW4 7NQ

A CIP catalogue record for this book is available from the British Library.

Papers used by Michael O'Mara Books Limited are natural, recyclable
products made from wood grown in sustainable forests. The manufacturing
processes conform to the environmental regulations of the country of origin.

ISBN: 978-1-84317-564-3

1 2 3 4 5 6 7 8 9 10

www.mombooks.com

Design by Design 23

Printed and bound in Finland by Bookwell, Juva

Stonehenge, Wiltshire, England

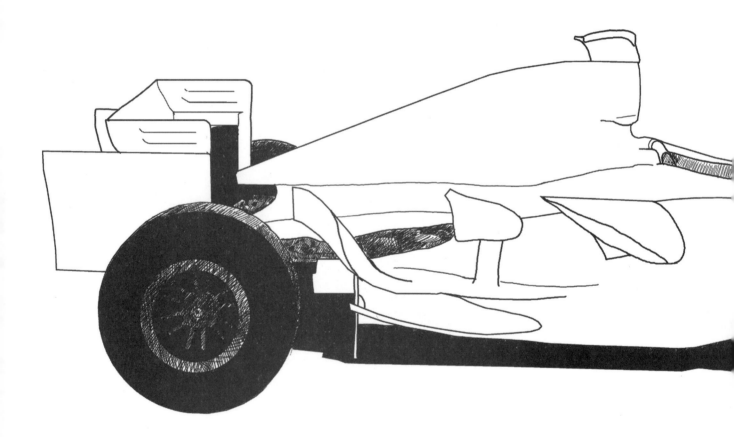

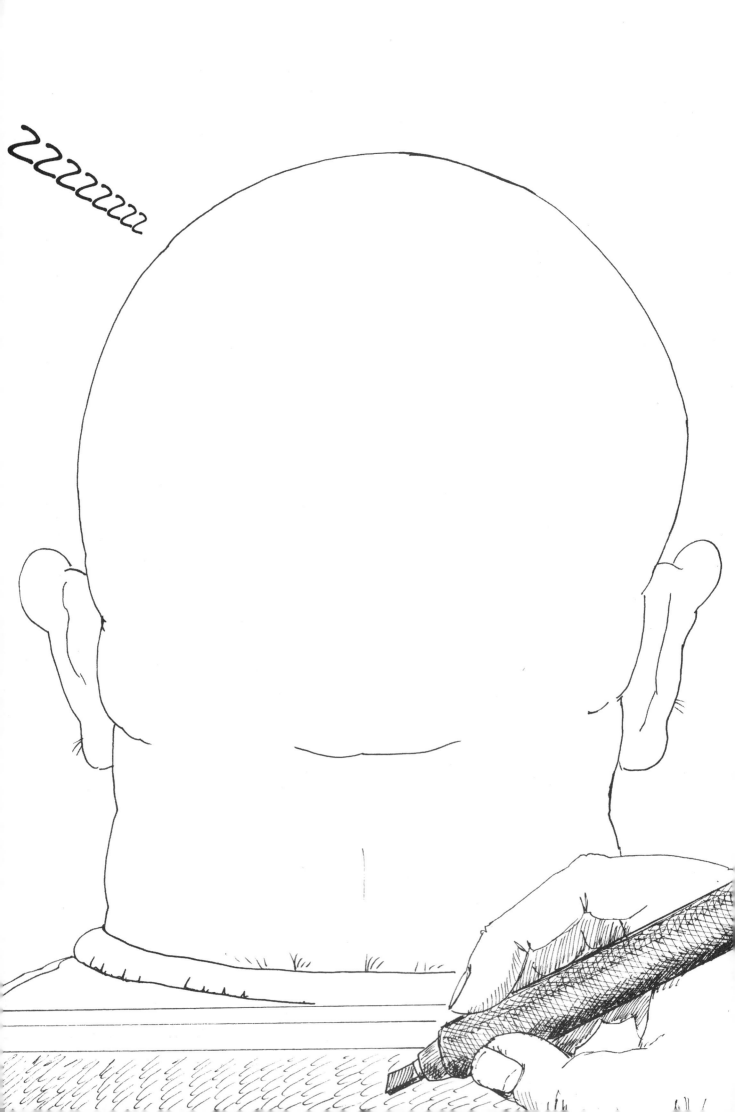

Houses of Parliament, London

I say, Frances, look what some rotter has done to our painting!

The Family Album

HMS *Dreadnought*

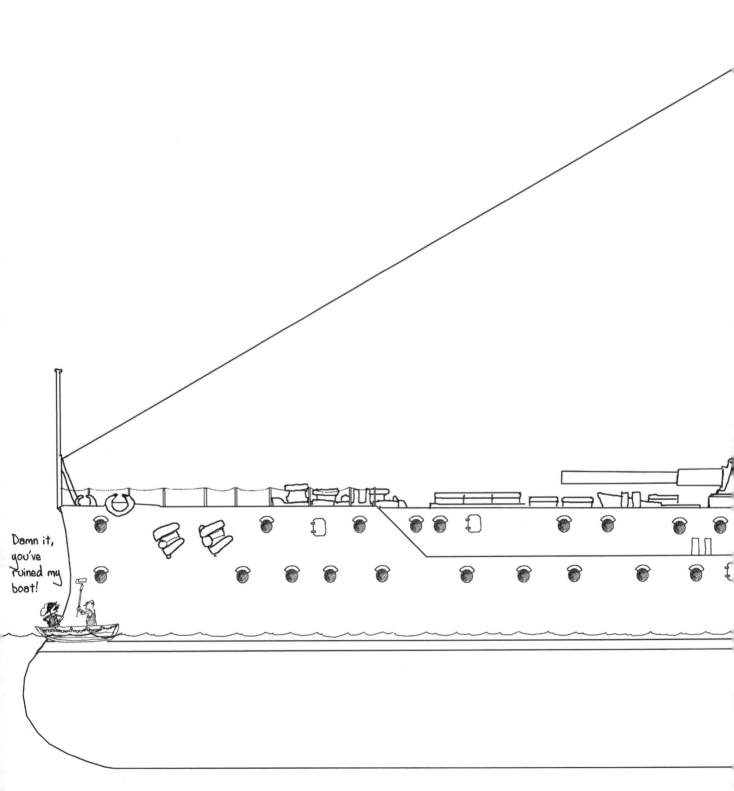

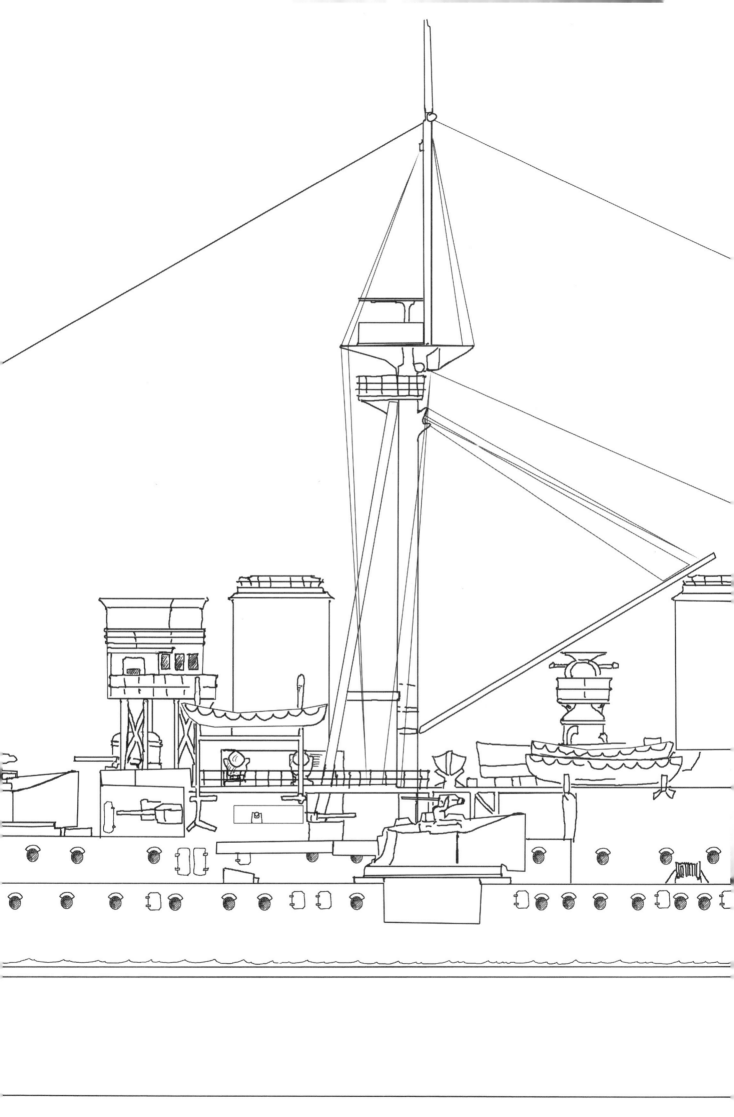

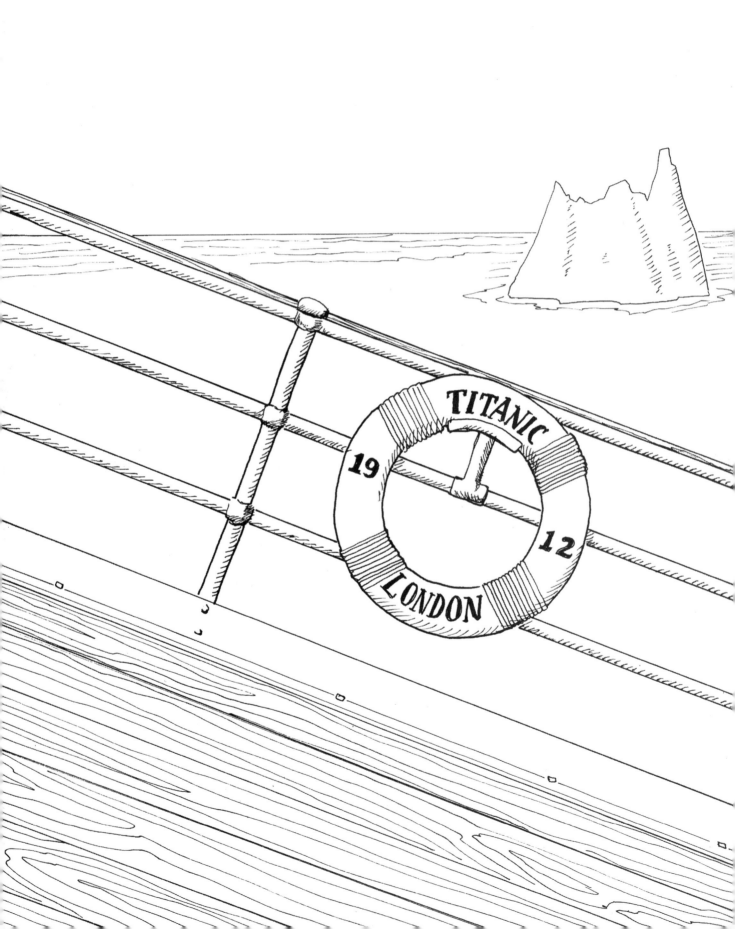

Château de Villandry, France

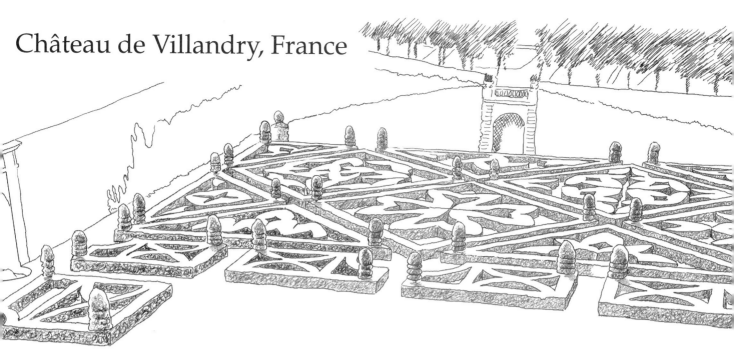

I'm sick of 'edges, get someone else to finish it.

Casablanca (1942)

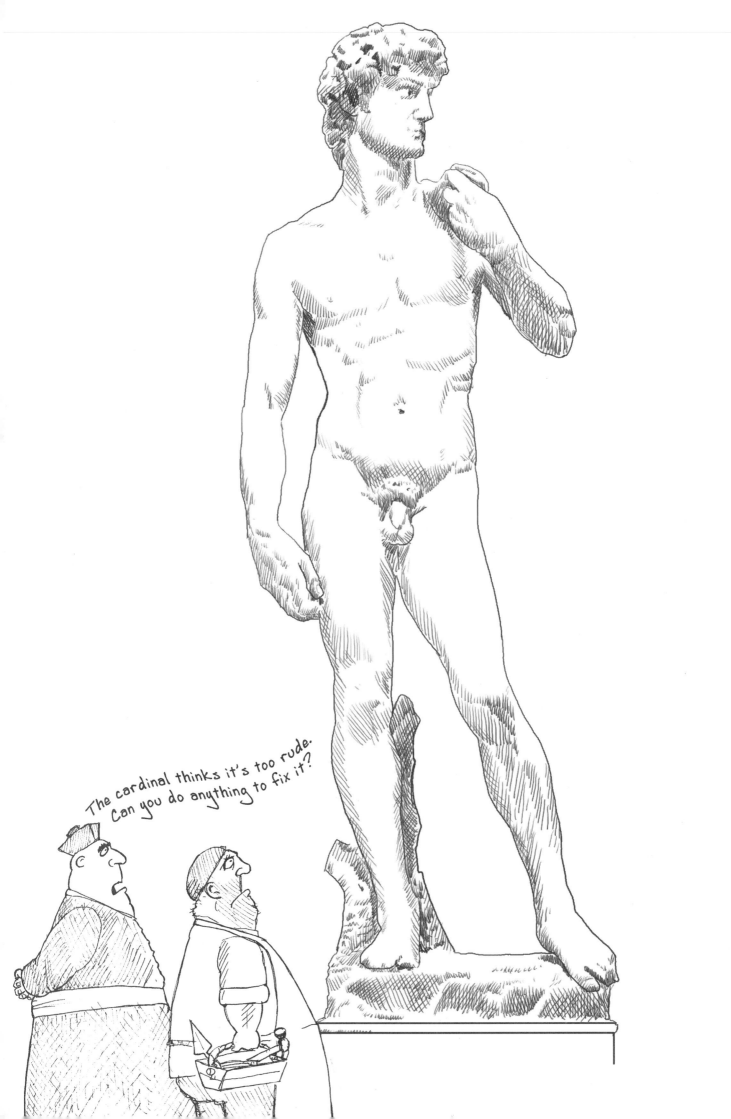

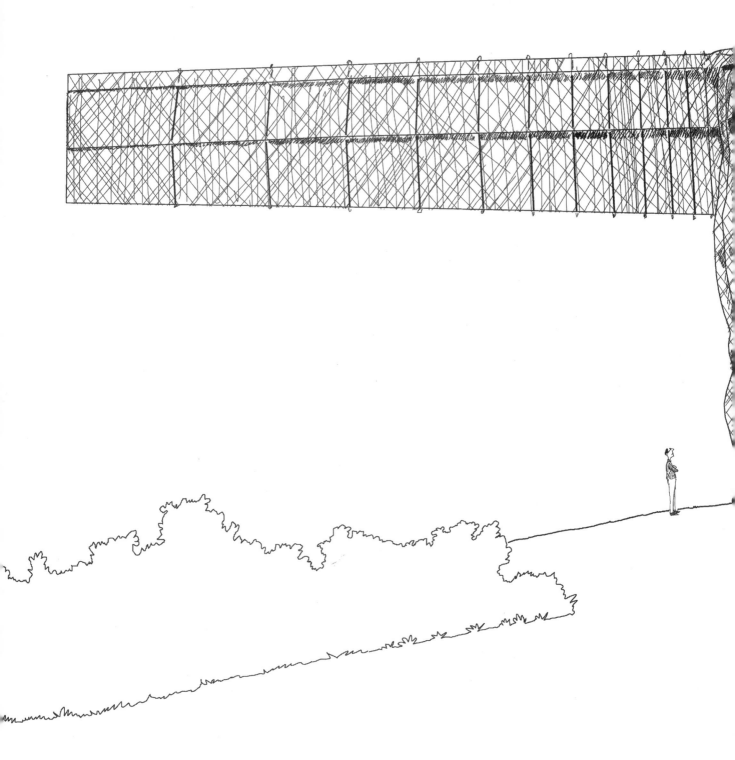

The Angel of the North, Anthony Gormley (1998), Gateshead, England

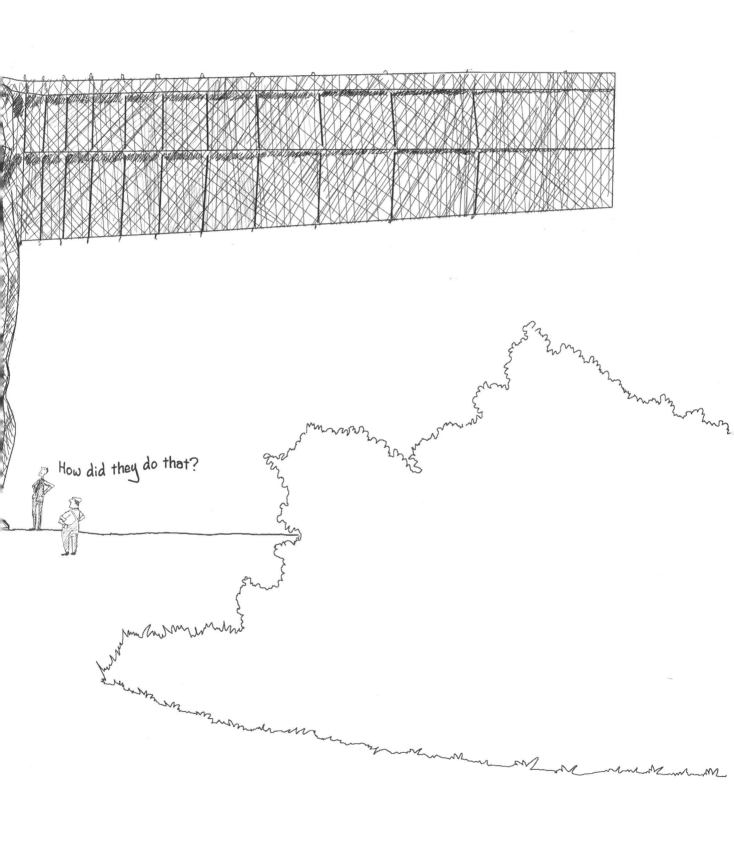

Quick, now's your chance!

Captain Cook, 1930 travel poster

Bayeux Tapestry, death of King Harold

Time for a bit of embroidered graffiti!

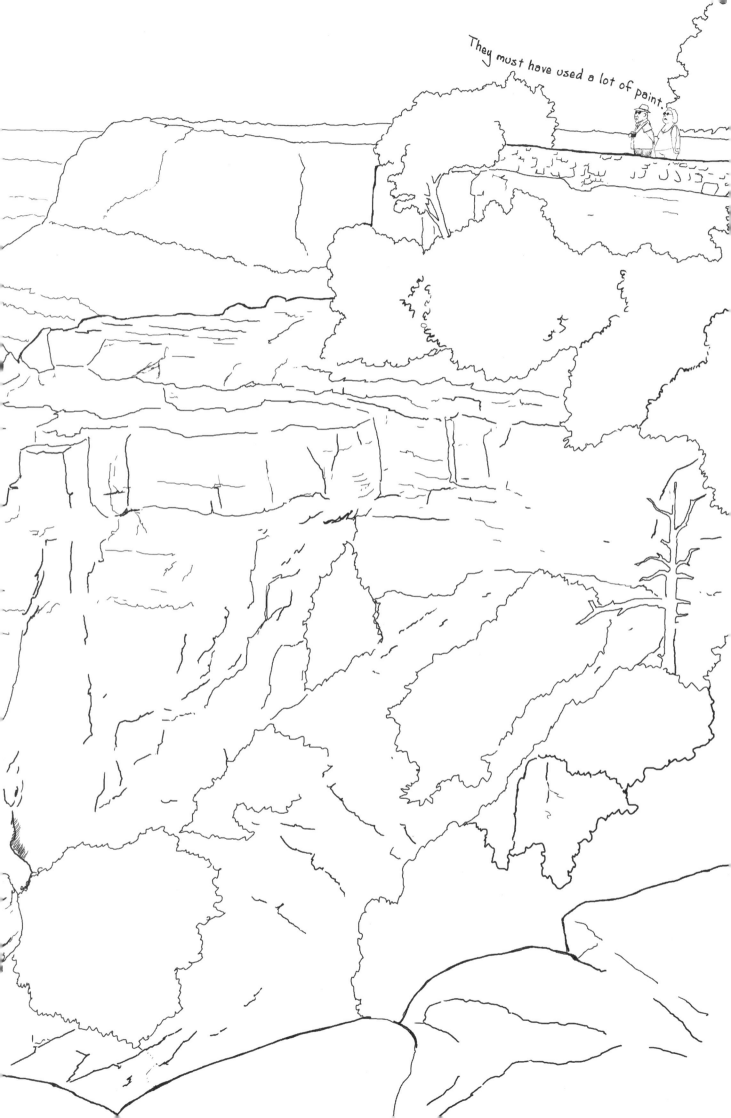

Gustave Doré, illustration for Milton's *Paradise Lost*

What's he making such a fuss about?

G Doré

Tutankhamun

The Empire State Building, New York

Buckingham Palace, London

Daddy, what did YOU do in the Great War?

Mount Rushmore, South Dakota, USA

Plenty of room for more heads here.

Otto von Bismarck

Outrageous!

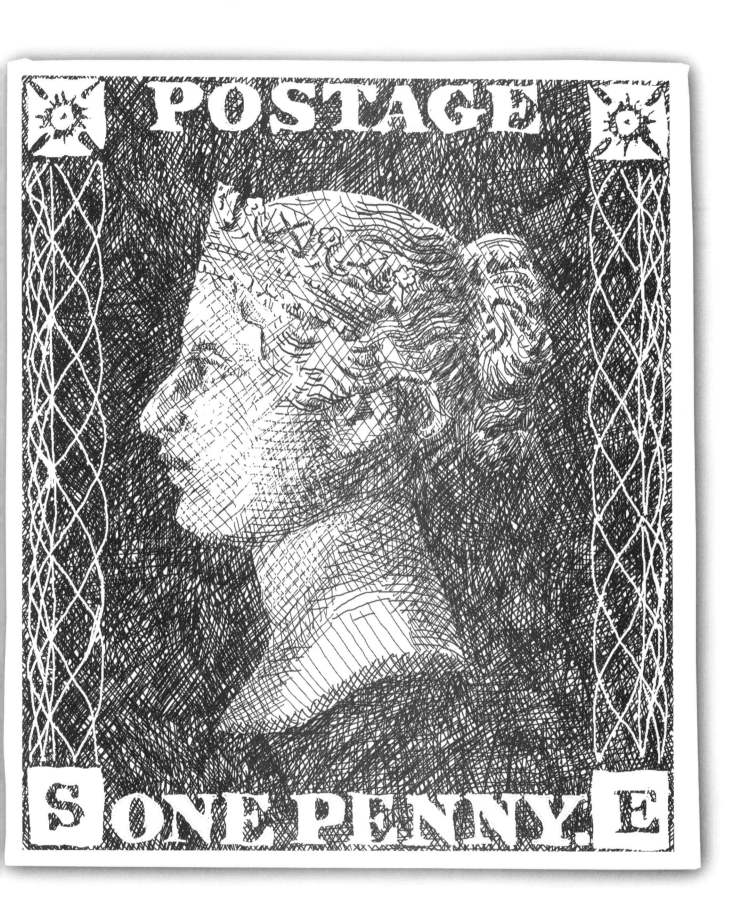

Penny Black, 1840

'The Gherkin' (30 St Mary Axe), London

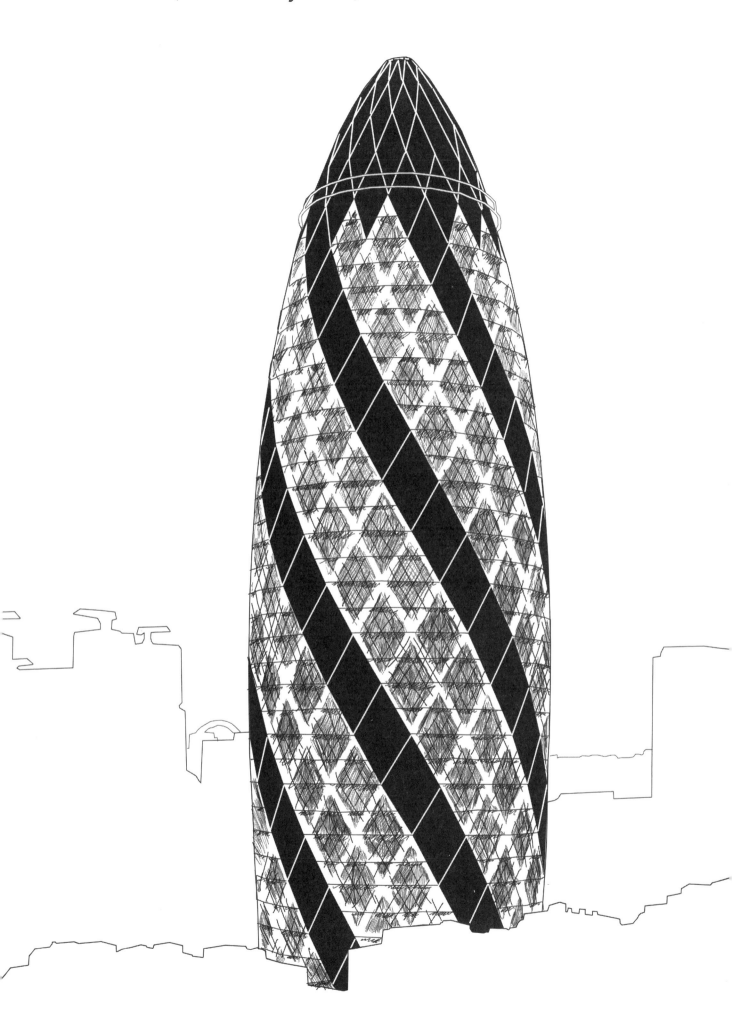

Palace of Versailles, France

Gin Lane,
William Hogarth,
(1750)

Cerne Abbas giant, Dorset, England

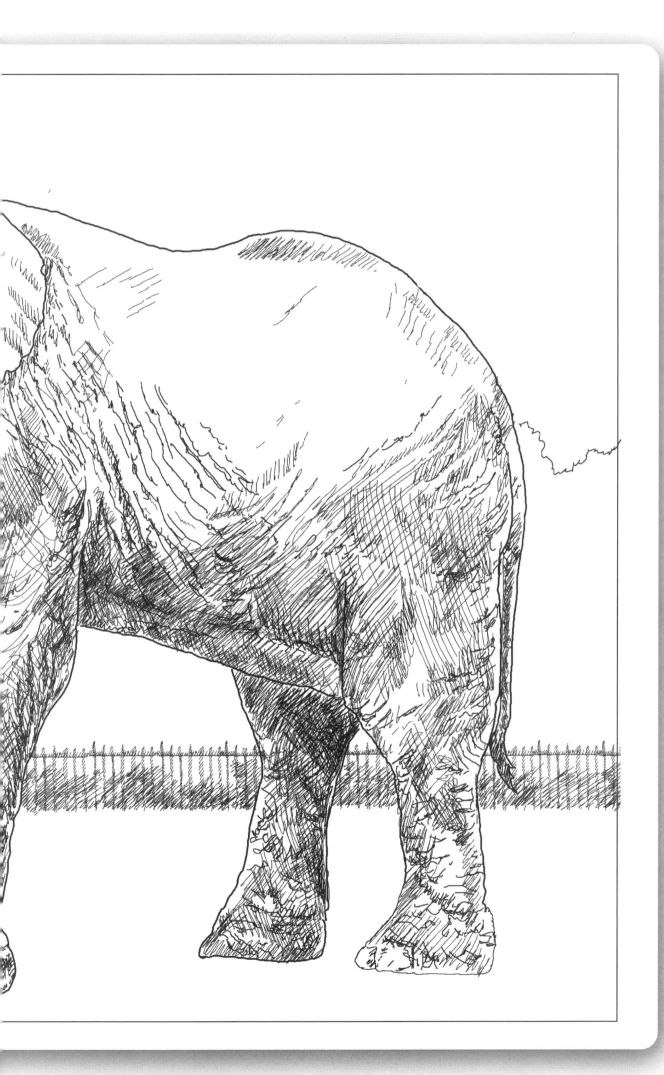

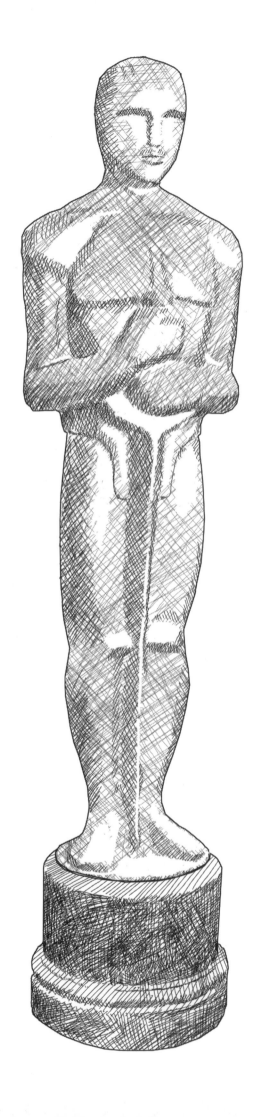

HASTA LA VICTORIA SIEMPRE

Boudicca and Her Daughters,
Thomas Thornycroft (1902), London

It's getting a bit tatty.
Give it a make-over and cheer it up.

'Danse Macabre', *Nuremberg Chronicle* (1493)

Plenty of room for more!

The Three Graces, Peter Paul Rubens (*c*.1636)

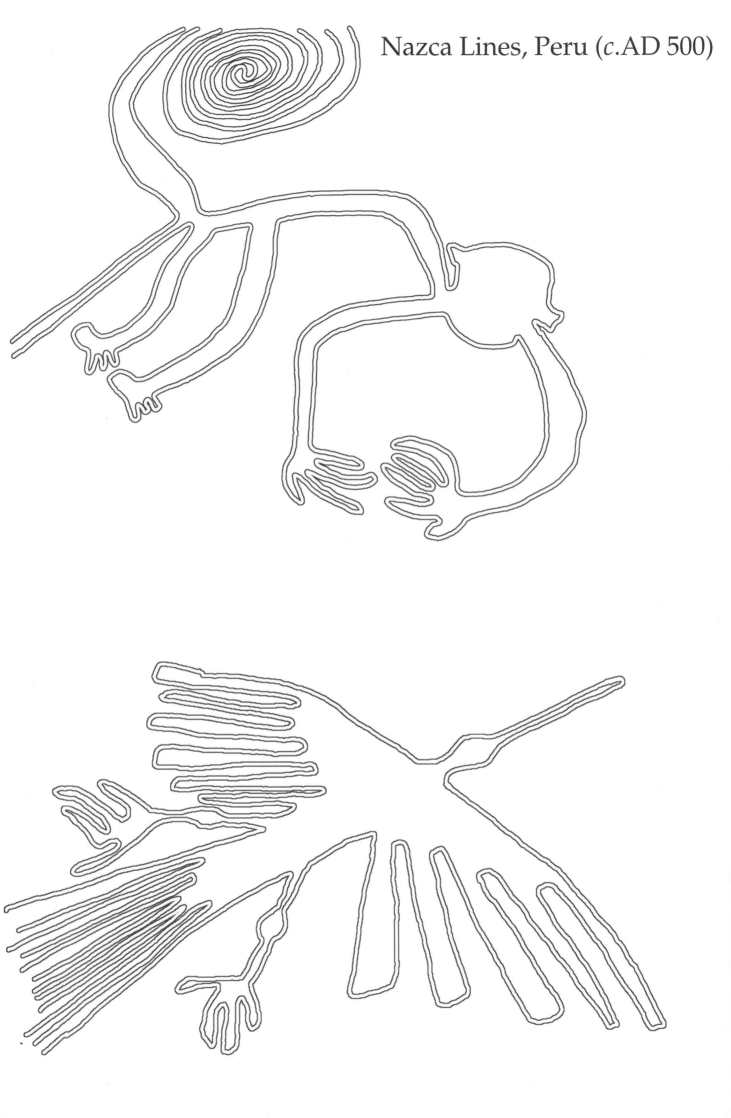

Nazca Lines, Peru (*c*.AD 500)

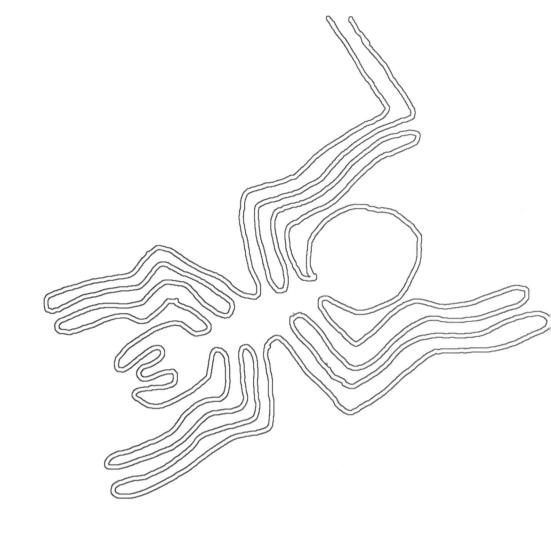

Hoover Dam, Ohio, USA

Arrangement in Grey and Black, James McNeill Whistler (1871)

World Cup, 1966

Cave painting, Lascaux, Dordogne, France

How many times? Don't paint on the walls.

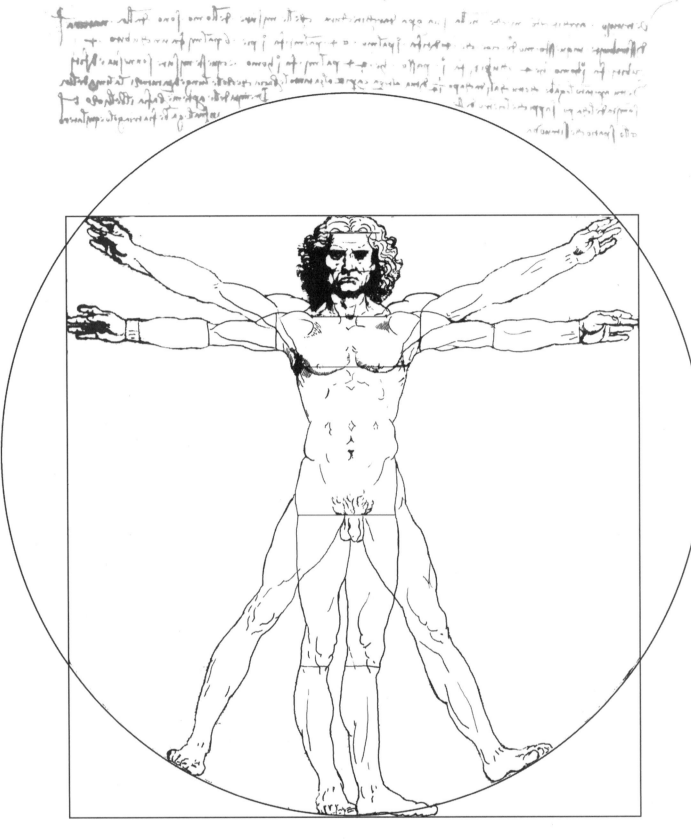

The Great Wall of China

Opera House, Sydney, Australia

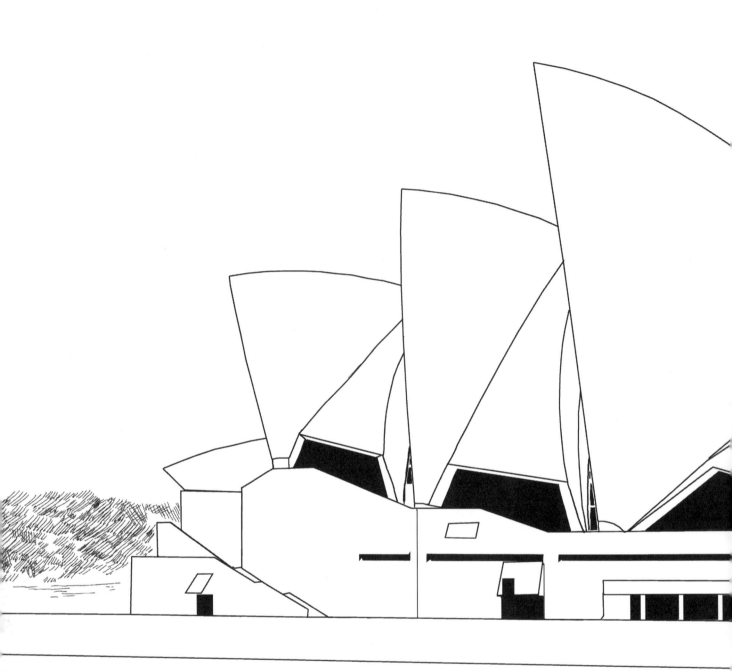

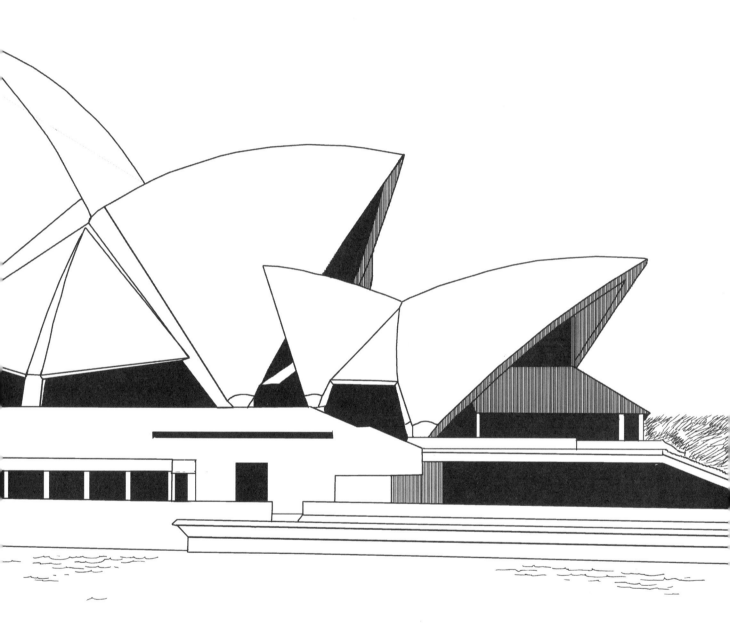

Uluru (Ayer's Rock), Northern Territory, Australia

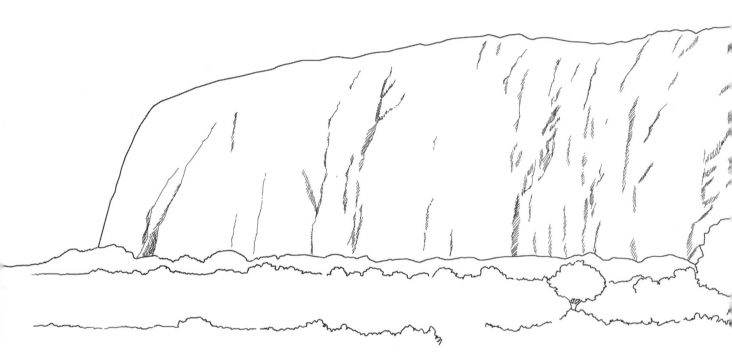

Bloody tourists!

Superman #1, 1939

Main entrance, Old Trafford, Manchester

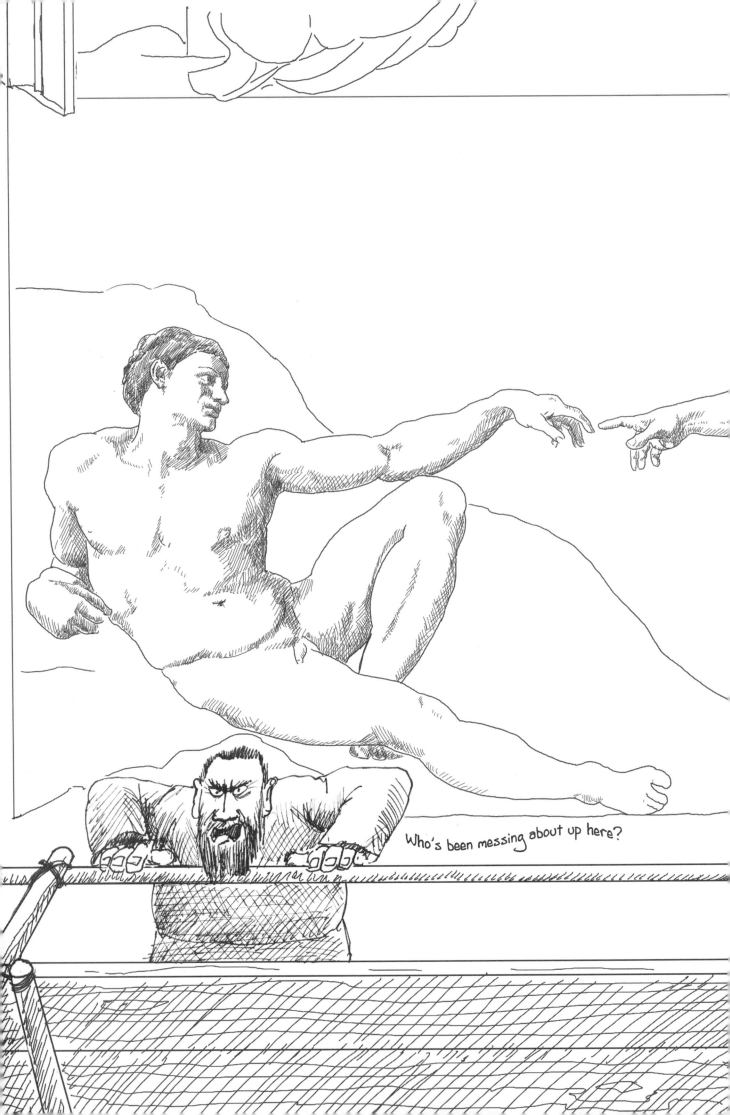

Fort Knox, Kentucky, USA

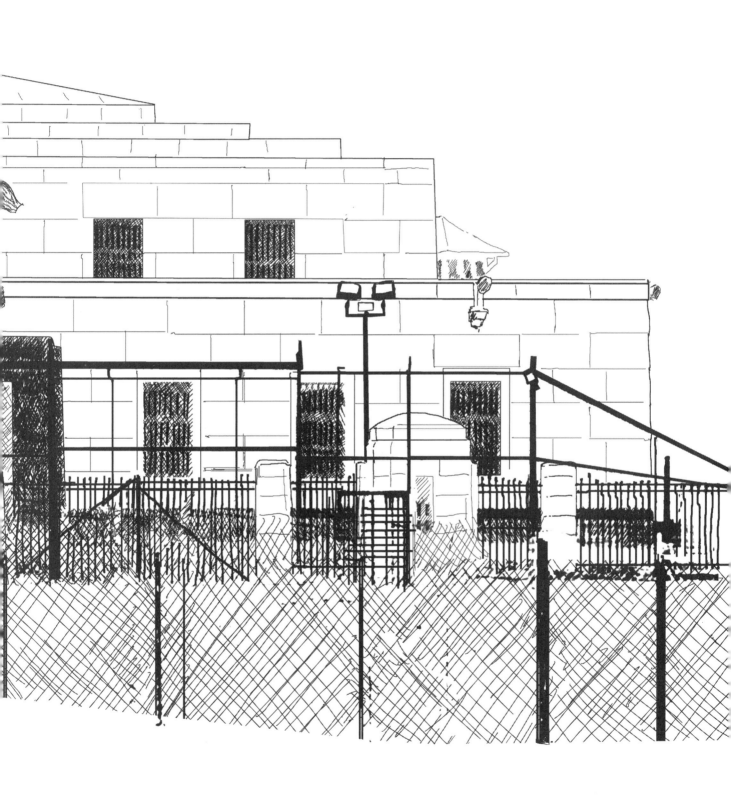

Wasn't me ....

FV 4201 Chieftain tank (1960–70s)

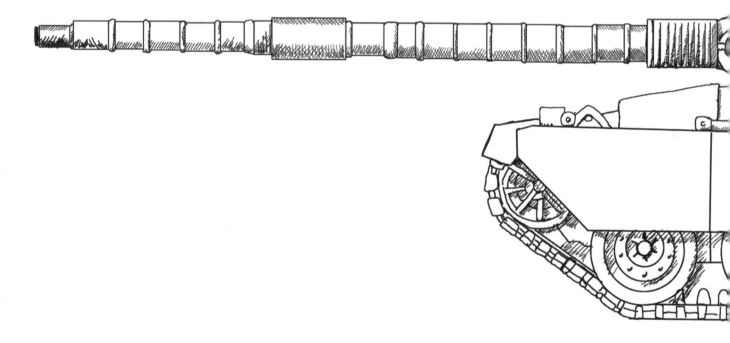

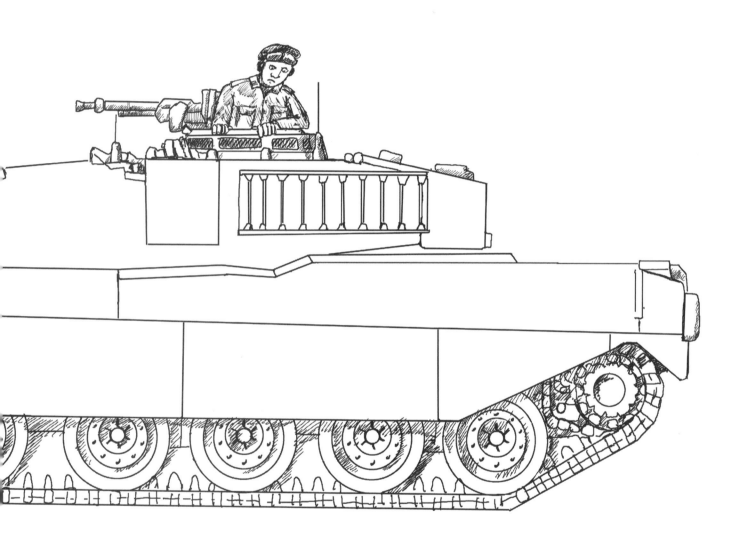

Papyrus of Ani (*c*.1240 BC)

Cave painting, Barranco de la Valltorta, Spain

Bring these 10,000-year-old paintings uo to date.

The White Cliffs of Dover

LVDCI DAVID
1812

OPVS

Bank of England, London

Tarzan

Irish State Coach

United Nations Headquarters, New Yo

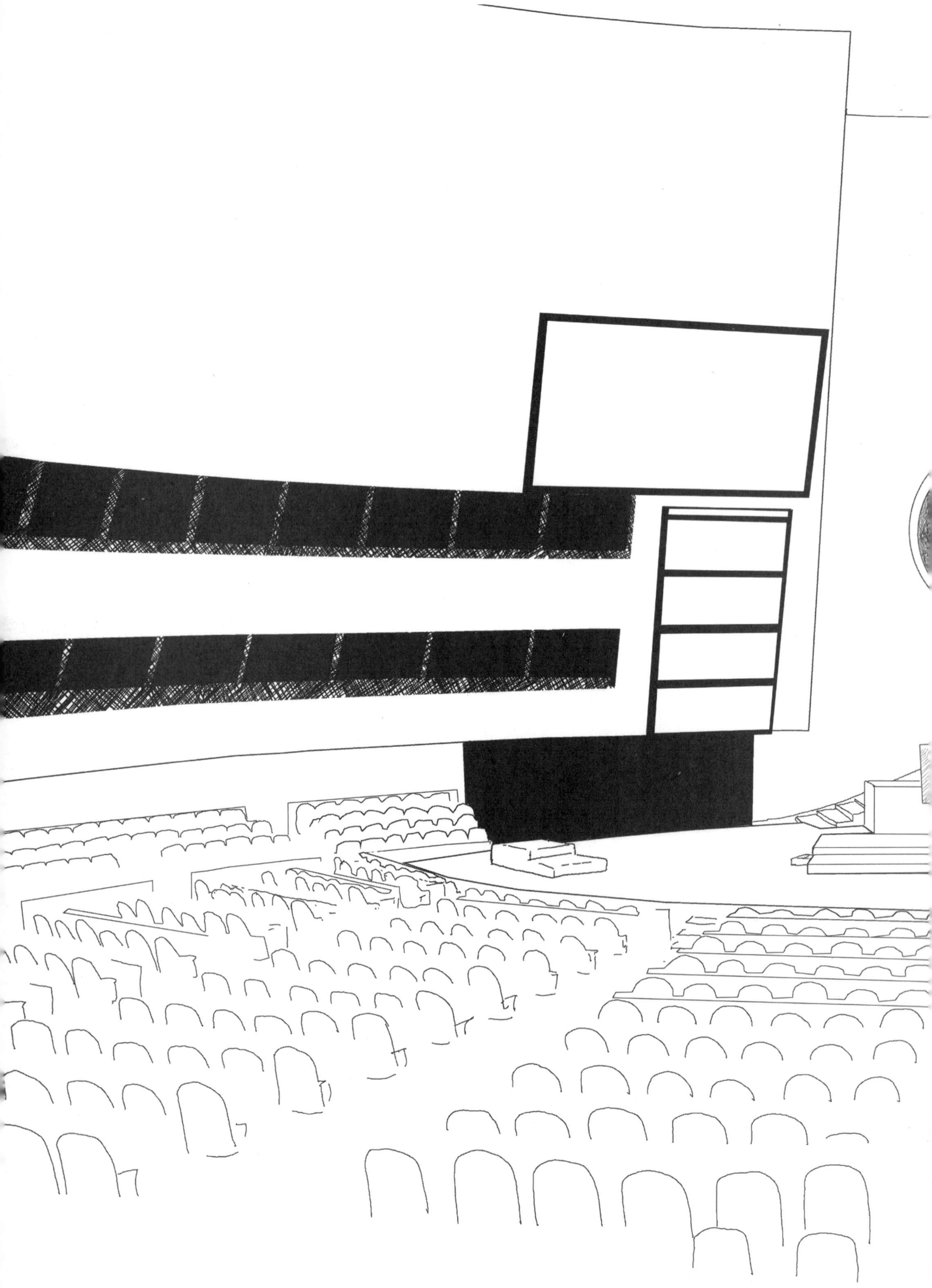

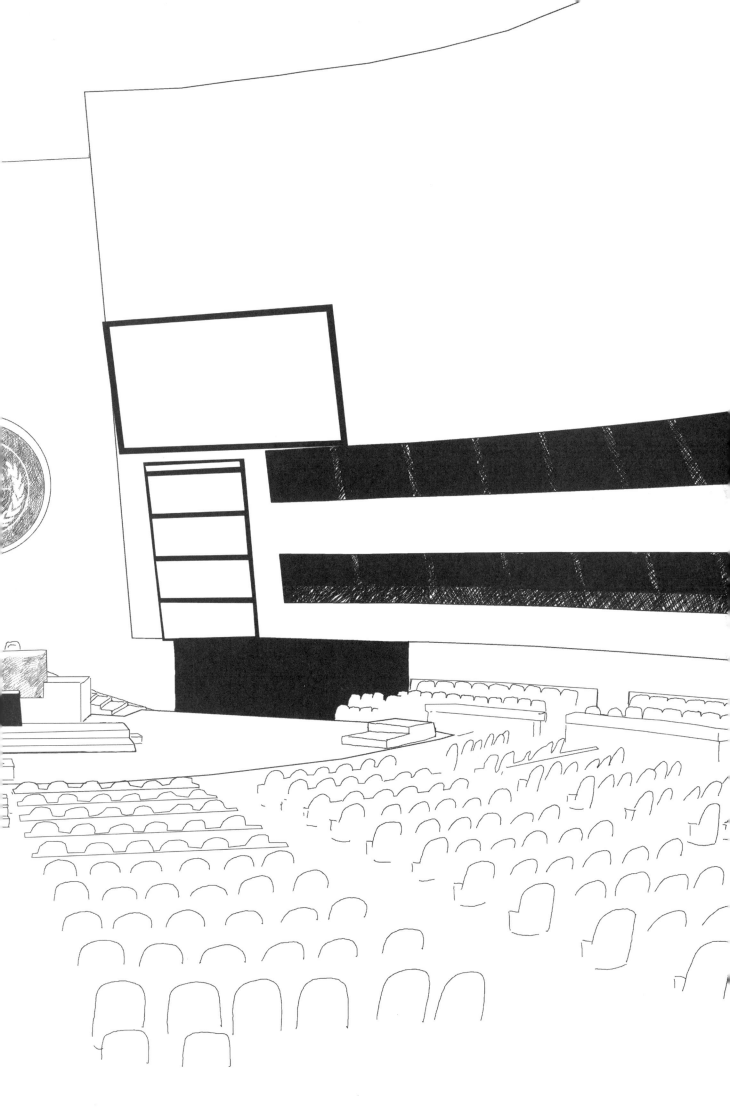

Venus of Willendorf (*c*.22,000 BC)

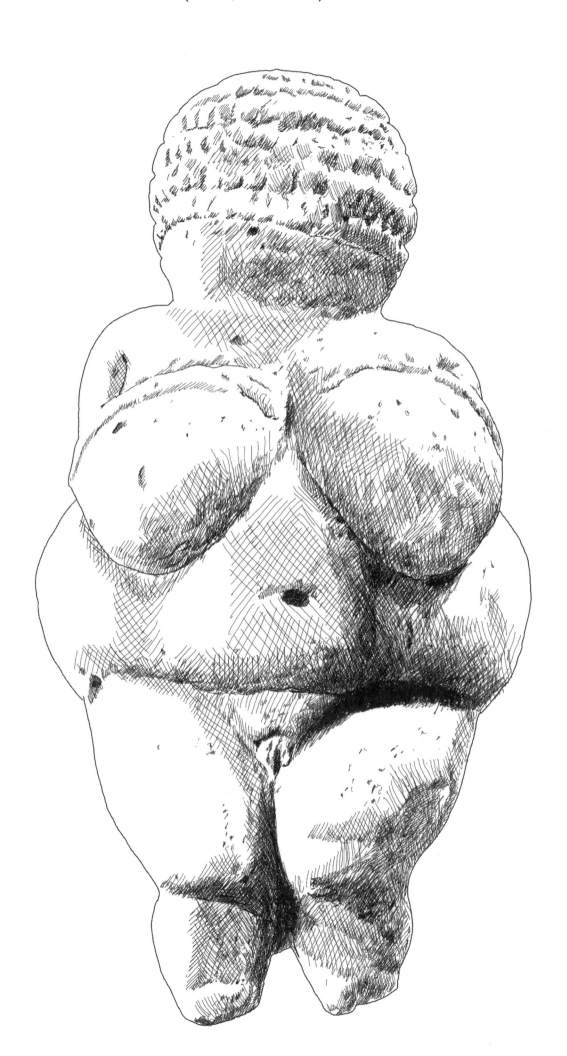

Entrance, Tower of London

The decorators are having a tea-break

Sight screen, Lord's Cricket Ground, London

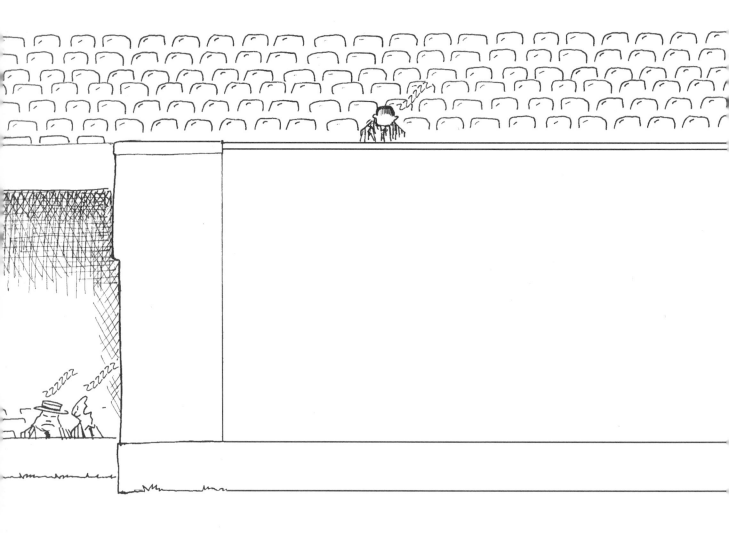

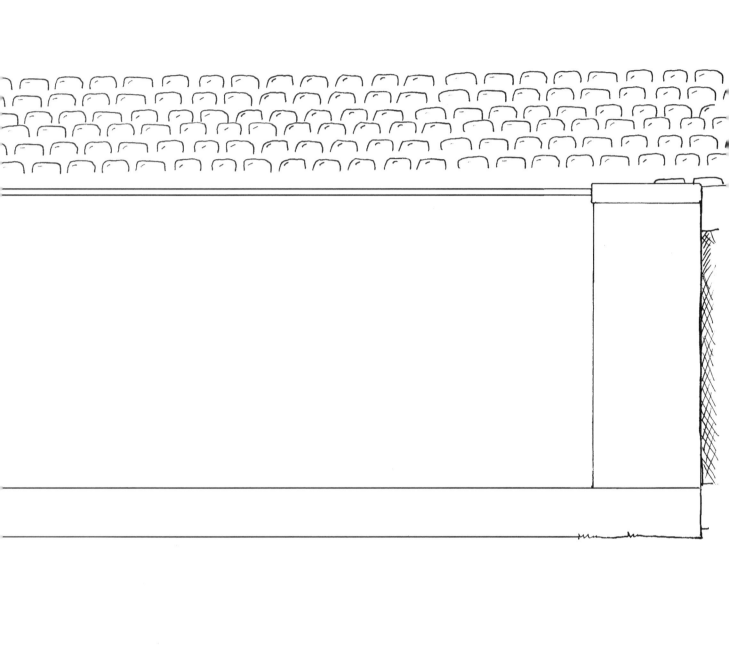

Go on, I dare you.

Gone With the Wind

The hills are alive . . .

No. 10 Downing Street, London

Cartes-de-visite

Mahatma Gandhi, 1931

The Beatles, Abbey Road, London

Cadillac, 1959

Topiary Garden, Hampton Court Palace, Richmond, Greater London

I'll leave my clippers there while I'ave a nice cup of t

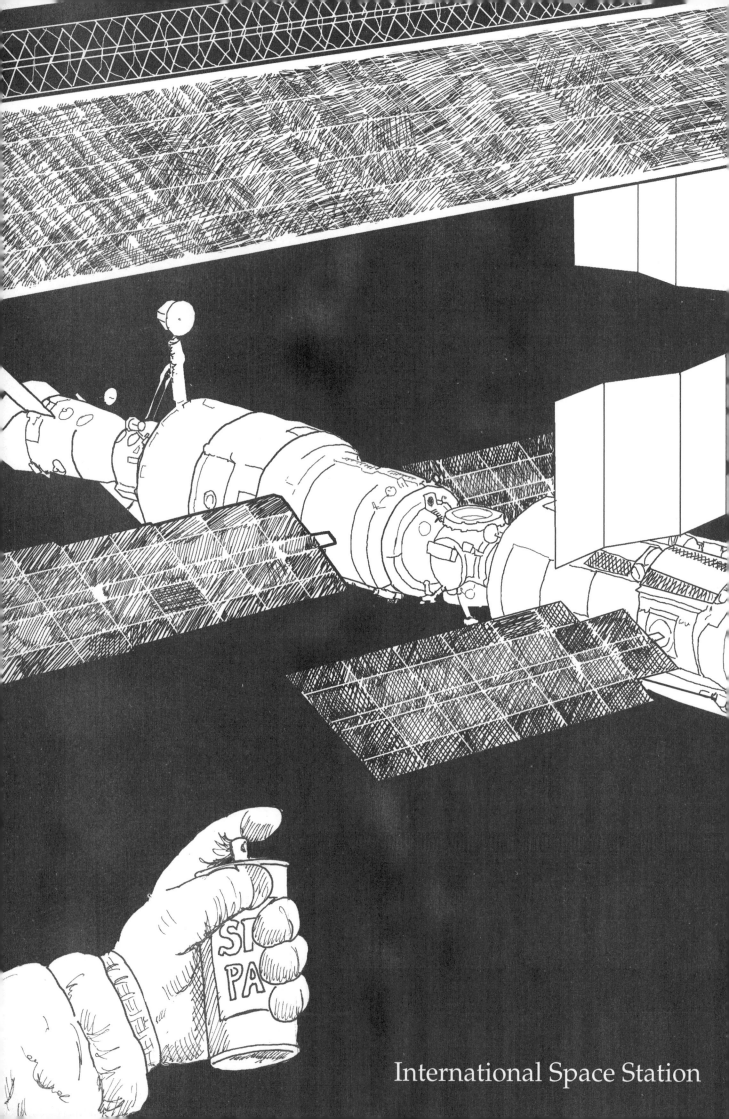

International Space Station

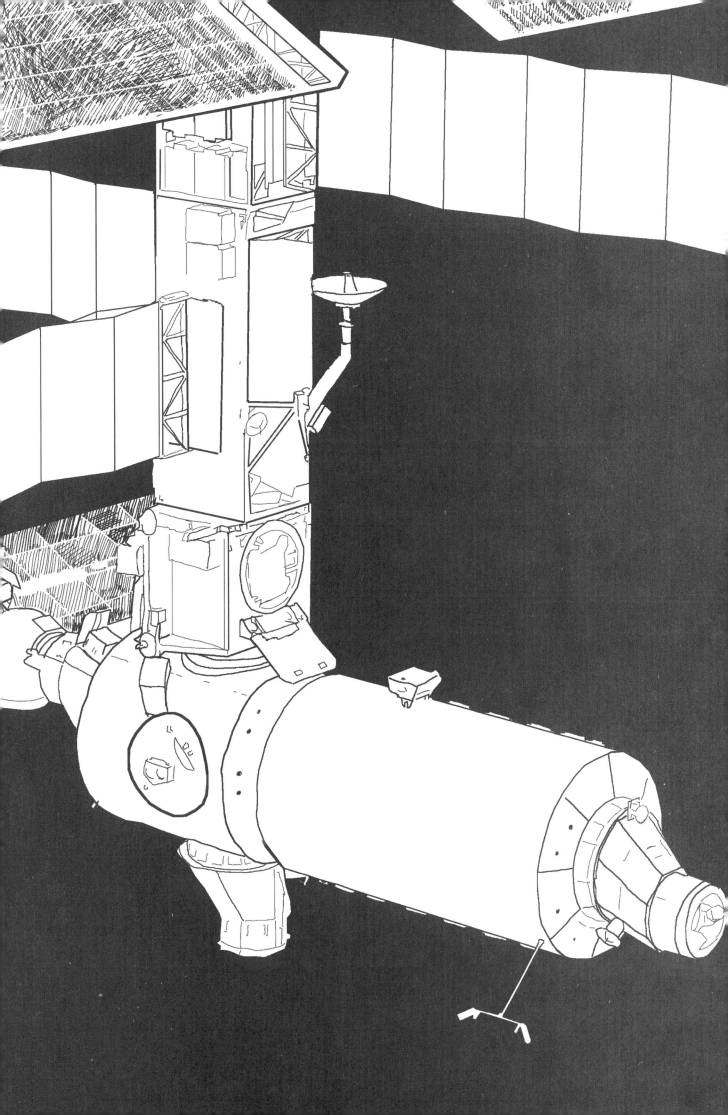

The Popemobile

Rungrado May Day Stadium, North Korea

The Pentagon, Arlington County, Virginia, USA

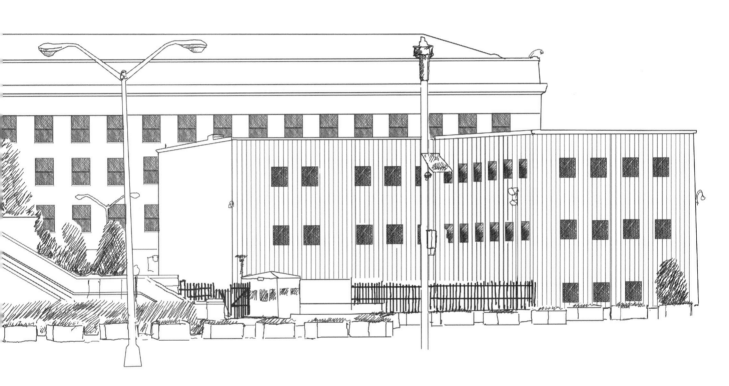

St Basil's Cathedral, Red Square, Moscow

Bedroom in Arles,
Vincent van Gogh (1888)

Doge's Palace, Venice

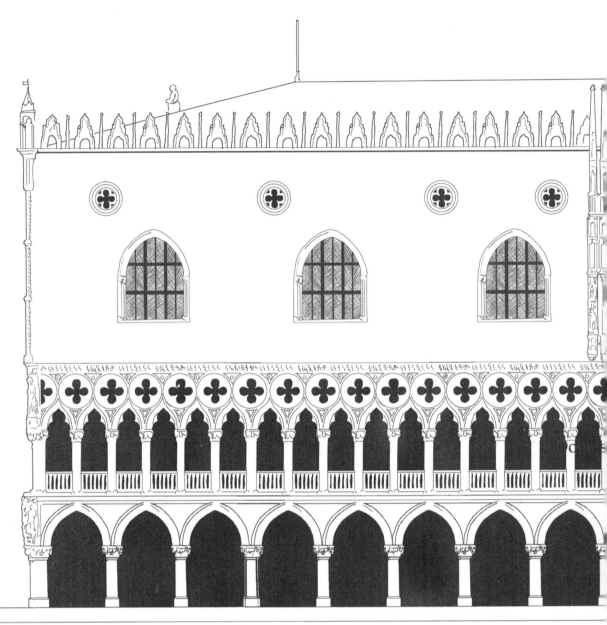

What have thay done to the Palace?

Washington Crossing the Delaware,
Emanuel Gottlieb Leutze (1851)

Give the monk a surprise when he comes back

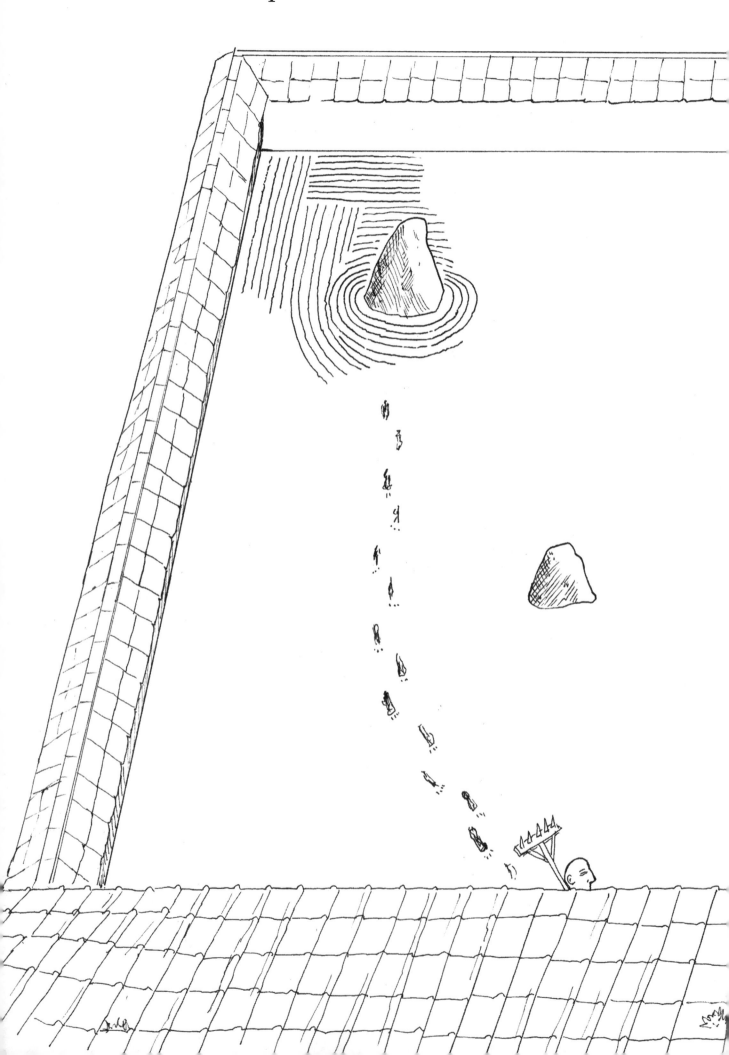

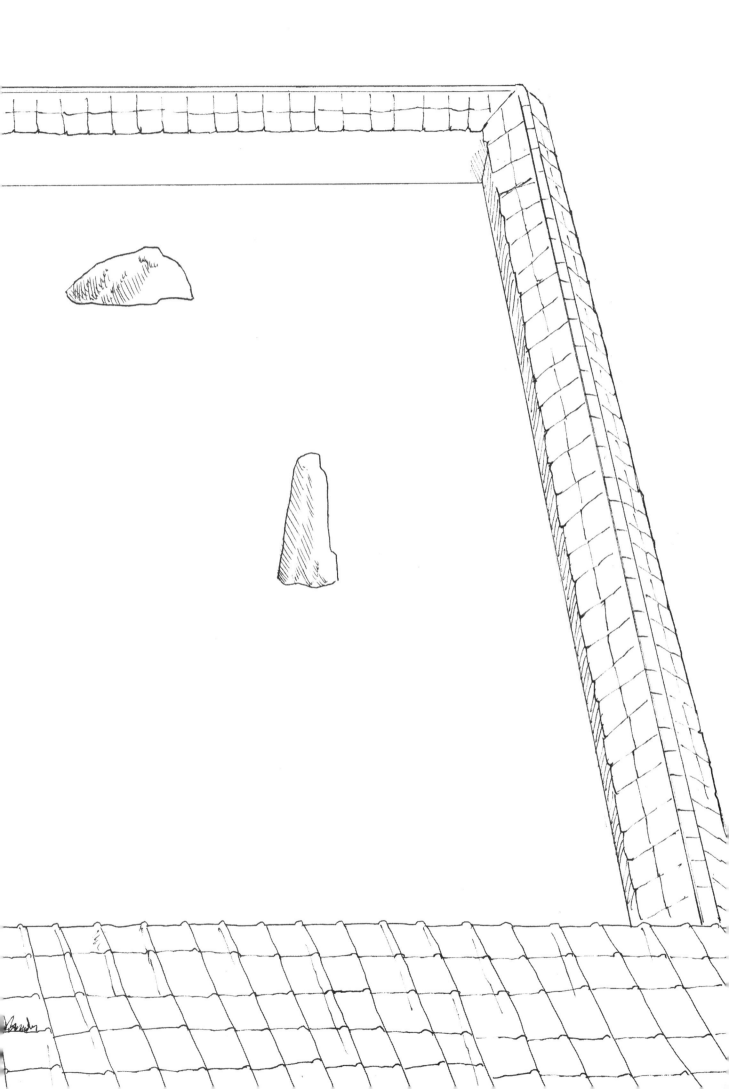

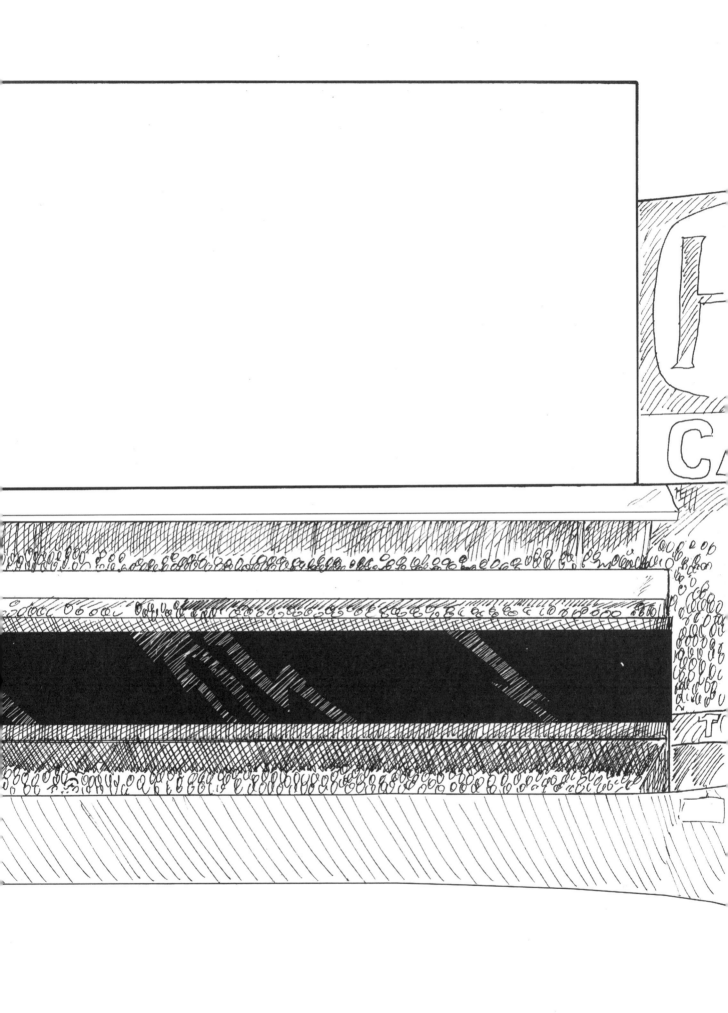

Who has got control of the giant video screens?